Olive

written by
Michelle E. Wilson

Michelle E. Wilson

illustrated by
Angie Penrose

Angie Penrose

pink umbrella
books

ISBN: 978-1-949598-08-7 (paperback)
ISBN: 978-1-949598-10-0 (hardcover)

Published by Pink Umbrella Books (www.pinkumbrellapublishing.com)

Michelle E. Wilson, author
 Olive / Michelle E. Wilson

  A little lamb learns that her family still loves her, despite all of the mistakes she makes.

Library of Congress Control Number:2019946055
Illustrations by Angie Penrose
Illustrations © 2019 Angie Penrose

Edited by Merry Gordon and Marnae Kelley

Curriculum created by:
Sereh Haubrich, Special Education Teacher
Nina Markey, Elementary School Principal
Michelle E. Wilson, Educator

Dedicated
to ~~Olive Ewe~~
all of you!

Michelle and Angie's official bios:

Michelle lives in the Northwest with her family, three indoor dogs, and a totally stuck-up cat. And somehow, they all get along. She writes inspirational nonfiction and women's fiction. *Olive* is her first children's book and the most fun to write. *Olive* came to life in a poem Michelle wrote for her adoptive daughter as a way to express unconditional love for her. Family, faith, and fun are important to Michelle. She loves watching movies, playing Guitar Hero, and taking long walks to the fridge. You can find her at www.michellewilsonwrites.com

Angie is a married mom of three spicy boys. She is an artist at heart, with interests spanning from drawing to painting, crafts, and photography. She runs a successful photography business. *Olive* is her first illustrated book. She loves watching movies and reading books. She has a collection of crayons her children aren't allowed to touch and loves everything Disney. Like, a crazy amount of love. You can find her at www.angiepenrose.com

But we like our bios by Finley, age 7, better:

Michelle is nice to other people, even if she doesn't know them. She writes books for moms and women too. She's kind of funny sometimes. If she were a cookie, she'd be a chocolate chip cookie maybe.

Aunt Angie is a good artist. She is nice. Her pictures are really good. Well, she's kinda short, but that's okay. I like her because she does crafts with me. If she were an animal, she would be a unicorn.

One day there was a happy lamb whose name was Olive Ewe.

And even though
she tried real hard
things often went askew.

One time she spilled her cereal
and turned the carpet blue.

Her father's face, it grew so red
as he said,

She tried to make a card for Mom
with glitter and some glue.

The paper stuck
right to her hair,

and Mom sighed,

"Olive Ewe."

So Olive cleaned
her messy curls,

then played with Spencer Roo.

She threw a ball
that hit his head
and he yelled,

"OLIVE EWE!"

Olive stayed
outside to think
until the rain
was through.

She stepped into a mud puddle
and mumbled,

While playing at her grandma's house,
sweet Olive lost her shoe.

She found it under Grandpa's hat.
He groaned,

That night she sat down for a meal,
her favorite, clover stew.

Her bowl flew onto
Brother's head.

He jumped.

"Hey, Olive
—ewwww!"

Then Olive took a bubble bath
with Sister's new shampoo.

When Sister saw it was all gone she frowned.

When Olive went to bed that night
she sure was feeling sad

'cause even though
she tried her best
some stuff just
turned out bad.

–Has
this ever
happened
to you?

Some didn't like
the things she did,
and this made her
more blue.

"Don't worry, dear,"
Mom gently said.

"We still love all of you."

Then Olive jumped atop her bed
and said, "It's really true!

With all my thumps and
lumps and bumps,

you all love

Olive

Ewe!"

Stop and Think: Feel

Being a kid means having lots of feelings. Big feelings. Small feelings. Good feelings. And feelings that are hard. Look at these pictures and see if you can answer these questions:

1. What is Olive feeling?
2. How are the others feeling?
3. How do you know?
4. When have you felt this way?
5. When is it important to understand feelings?

Stop and Think: Fix

Olive had some thumps and bumps and lumps. How did she fix them?

If you're like Olive, you've had some thumps and bumps and lumps along your way. Some thumps can be fixed fast. Some bumps take longer. And some lumps can't be fixed at all. But we can always do our best to make it better. You can follow Olive's example and fix yours, too.

1. Think about your part of the problem.
2. Say, "I'm sorry."
3. Think of a solution.
4. Try your best to fix it.

Stop and Think: Forgive

When someone hurts us, it can be hard to forgive them, even when they say they are sorry. Olive's family forgave her and she forgave them. You can forgive your friends and family, too, by following the example of Olive and her family and friends. When someone hurts your feelings and apologizes, you can:

1. Listen to their apology.
2. Tell them what they did.
3. Tell them how it made you feel.
4. Say, "I forgive you."
5. Let it go.

Made in the USA
Middletown, DE
03 January 2020

82279077R00020